DK READERS

LEARNING pre-level **1** TO READ

STAR WARS™

THE CLONE WARS™

Masters of the Force

Written by Jon Richards

These warriors are
Masters of the Force.
They use a special
power called the Force.

A Note to Parents

DK READERS is a compelling programme for beginning readers, designed in conjunction with leading literacy experts, including Maureen Fernandes, B.Ed (Hons). Maureen has spent many years teaching literacy, both in the classroom and as a consultant in schools.

Beautiful illustrations and superb full-colour photographs combine with engaging, easy-to-read stories to offer a fresh approach to each subject in the series. Each DK READER is guaranteed to capture a child's interest while developing his or her reading skills, general knowledg and love of reading.

The five levels of DK READERS are aimed at different reading abilities, enabling you to choose the books that are exactly right for your child:

Pre-level 1: Learning to read
Level 1: Beginning to read
Level 2: Beginning to read alone
Level 3: Reading alone
Level 4: Proficient readers

The "normal" age at which a child begins to read can be anywhere from three to eight years old. Adult participation through the lower levels is very helpful for providing encouragement, discussing storylines and sounding out unfamiliar words.

No matter which level you select, you can be sure that you are helping your child learn to read, then read to learn!

LONDON, NEW YORK, MUNICH,
MELBOURNE and DELHI

Editor Pamela Afram
Project Art Editor Clive Savage
Managing Editor Laura Gilbert
Design Manager Maxine Pedliham
Art Director Ron Stobbart
Publisher Simon Beecroft
Publishing Director Alex Allan
Pre-Production Producer Rebecca Fallowfield
Senior Producer Shabana Shakir
Jacket Designer Satvir Sihota

Designed and edited by Tall Tree Ltd
Designer Malcolm Parchment
Editor Jon Richards

Reading Consultant Maureen Fernandes

For Lucasfilm
Executive Editor Jonathan W. Rinzler
Art Director Troy Alders
Keeper of the Holocron Leland Chee
Director of Publishing Carol Roeder

First published in Great Britain in 2013 by
Dorling Kindersley Limited
80 Strand, London WC2R 0RL

2 4 6 8 10 9 7 5 3 1
001–187428–Jan/13

A CIP catalogue record for this book
is available from the British Library.

ISBN: 978-1-40936-784-0

Colour reproduction by Alta Image
Printed and bound by L-Rex, China

Discover more at
www.dk.com
www.starwars.com

Contents

The Force makes them
very strong fighters.
It also gives them
special talents.

Masters of the Force can be good or bad.

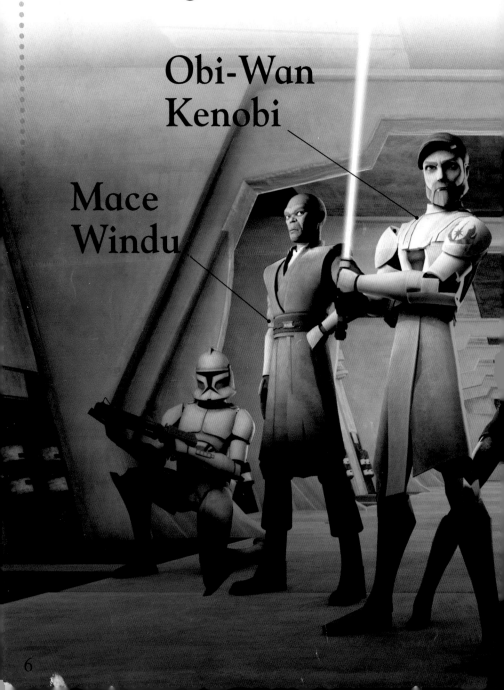

Obi-Wan Kenobi

Mace Windu

The good ones are called the Jedi.

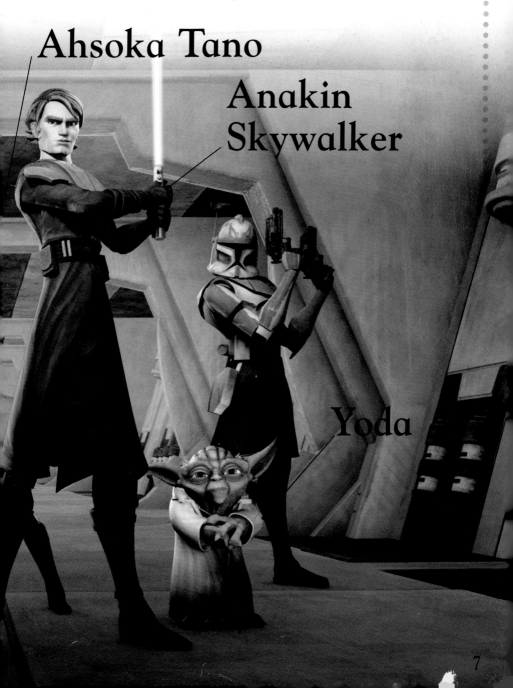

Ahsoka Tano

Anakin
Skywalker

Yoda

This is Jedi
Grand Master Yoda.
He is using the Force
to fight battle droids.

Yoda (YOH-DAH)

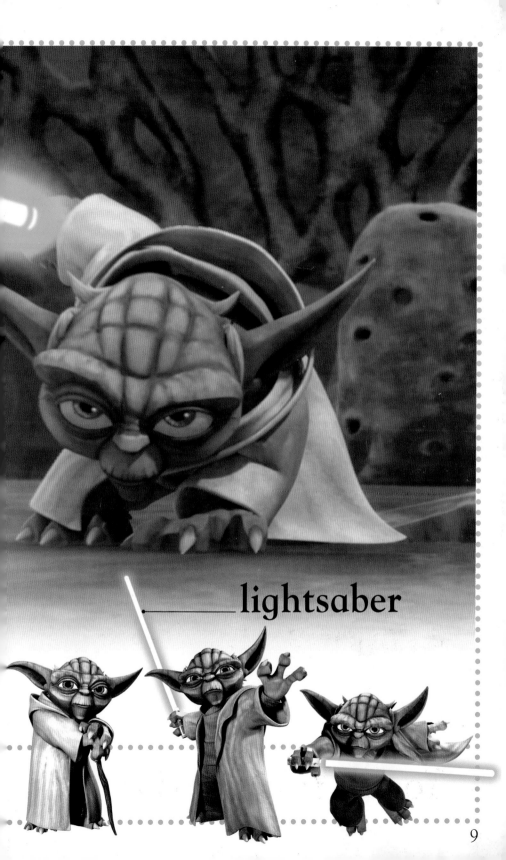

lightsaber

This is Jedi Knight Anakin Skywalker.

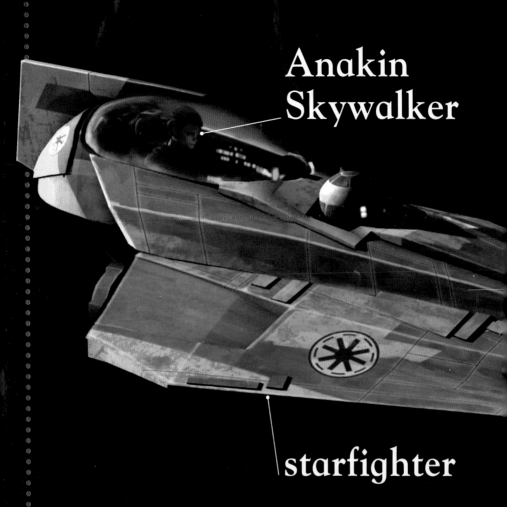

Anakin Skywalker

starfighter

Anakin Skywalker
(AN-A-KIN SKY-WAR-KER)

He is using the Force
to fly a starfighter
with amazing skill.

This is Jedi Master
Mace Windu.

clone trooper

Mace Windu
(MAYSS WIN-DOO)

He is using the Force
to shatter a windscreen
to save a clone trooper.

gunship

Quinlan Vos
(QWIN-LAN VOS)

This is Jedi Master
Quinlan Vos.
He is using the Force
to jump from a gunship.

This is Jedi general Obi-Wan Kenobi.

clone trooper

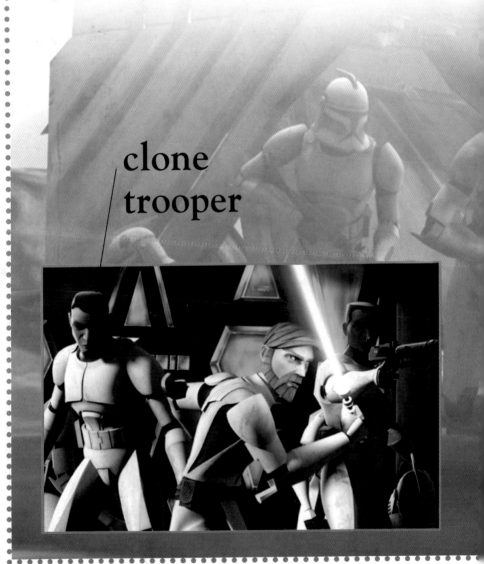

Obi-Wan Kenobi
(OH-BEE WON KE-NOH-BEE)

He is using the Force
to lead clone troopers
in battle.

armour

This is Jedi Padawan
Ahsoka Tano.

She is using the Force
to push commando
droids away from her.

Ahsoka Tano
(AH-SOH-KAR TAR-NOH)

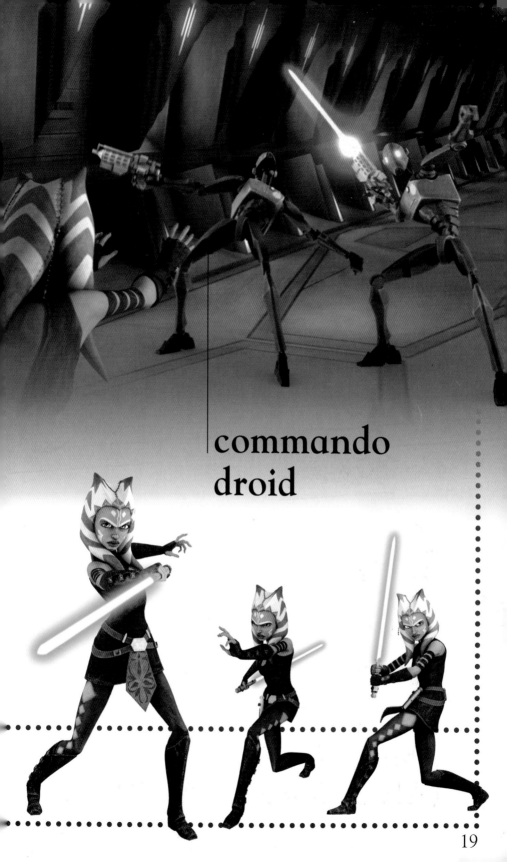

commando
droid

This is Jedi Master
Tera Sinube.

lightsaber

Tera Sinube
(TE-RAR SY-NOO-BEE)

He is using the Force to fight a criminal.

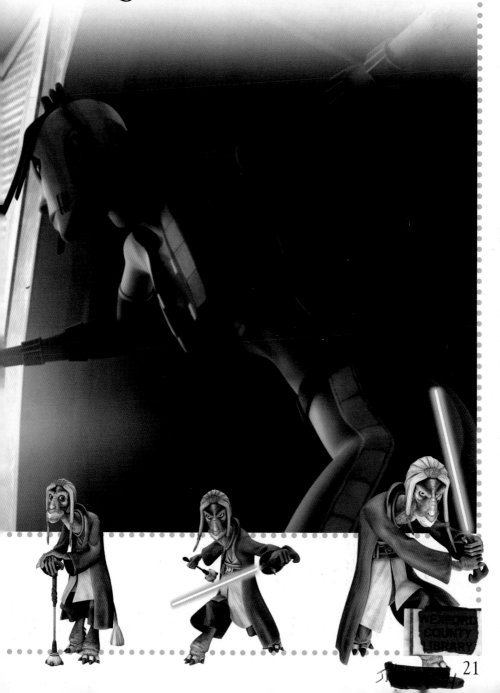

Not everyone uses
the Force for good,
like the Jedi.

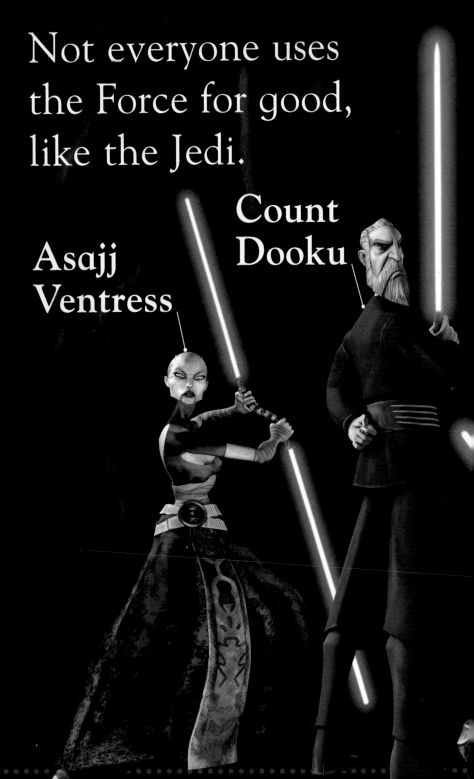

Count
Dooku

Asajj
Ventress

Some use the Force
for evil.
They are called
the Sith.

Darth
Maul

Savage
Opress

Darth Sidious is the strongest Sith.

Darth Sidious
(DARTH SID-EE-US)

He is using the Force
to shoot lightning
at his enemies.

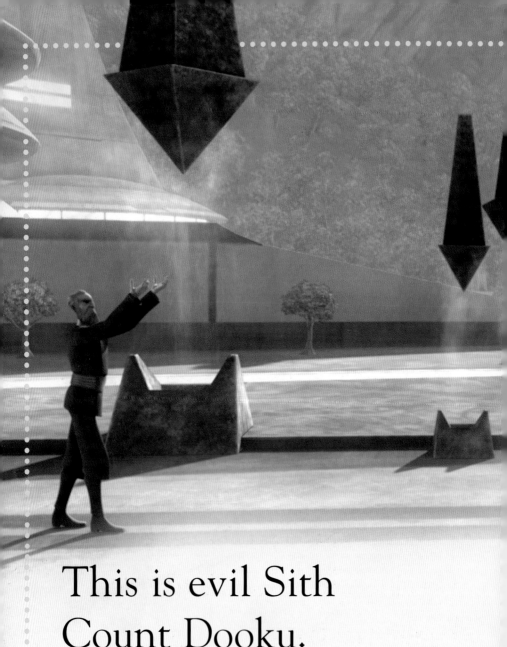

This is evil Sith
Count Dooku.

Count Dooku
(COUNT DOO-KOO)

Savage
Opress

He is using the Force to
teach Savage Opress
how to lift objects.

Ventress fights for the Sith.

Ventress
(VEN-TRESS)

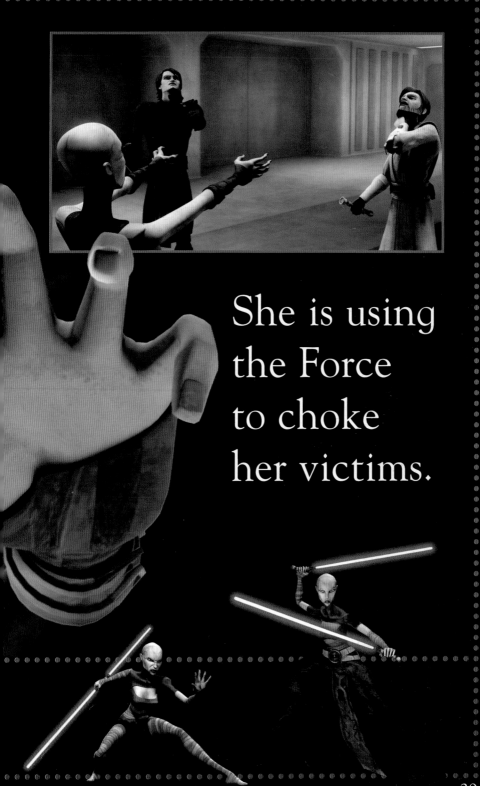

She is using
the Force
to choke
her victims.

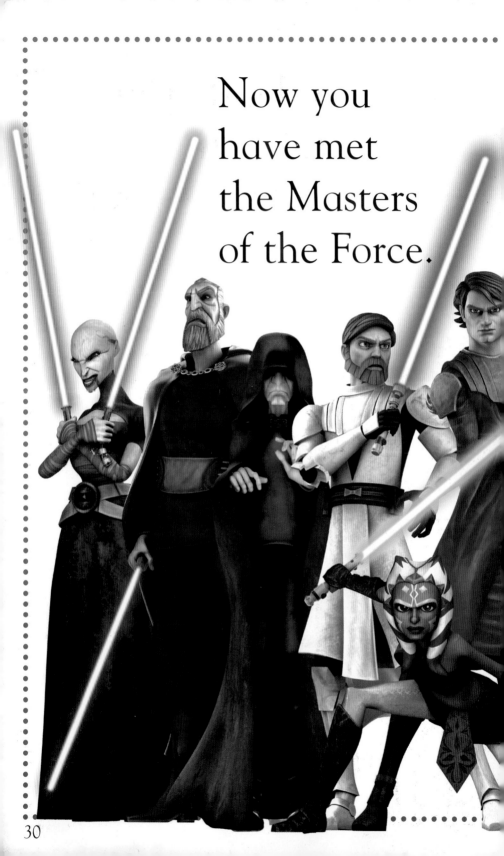

Now you
have met
the Masters
of the Force.

Who do you think is the most powerful?

Glossary

Clone troopers
A group of soldiers who are the same as each other.

Commando droid
A robot that is built to fight in wars.

Gunship
A large aircraft with lots of weapons.

Lightsaber
A special sword used by the Jedi and the Sith.

Starfighter
A small spacecraft that is used in battles.